Energetic Elliot

Susannah McFarlane Lachlan Creagh

A Scholastic Australia Book

This is Elliot, with
some of his friends—
Emma, Edvard,
Ethan and Eliza.

Elliot has enormous amounts of energy. He is the most energetic emu on the entire earth. Elliot is extremely eager and likes everything!

Elliot excitedly plays elastics with Eliza and Emma under the eucalypts, while the elderly emus enjoy their eclairs. He is also an essential member of the Eastern Emu Eleven.

Elliot's energy is endless!

He is extremely entertaining as Elvis, with his echidna entourage!

Elliot is also an energetic eater.

He eats everything, which is excellent,
but he especially loves eggplant
enchiladas with extra edam cheese.

Then early one evening there
was an event . . .

not quite an emergency,
but definitely an episode.

Elliot was exceptionally emotional.

He would not see eye-to-eye with anyone, not even Ethan.

Elliot was **exasperated!**

Elliot's energy was ebbing.

It was extinguished.

It had evaporated!

'Eek!' exclaimed Edvard.
'Eek! Eek!' exploded Emma.

'Eek! Eek! Eek!' echoed everyone else.

The doctor, an elegant, elderly eagle, entered and examined Elliot.

It was easy to explain—Elliot was exhausted! 'No exercises,' exclaimed the doctor, 'and no excursions. No excuses!'

It was not easy, but with enormous effort,
and Eliza and Ethan's encouragement,
Elliot closed his eyes . . . and eventually
slept for the entire evening.

Then Elliot was full
of energy again!

Now each and every
evening Elliot ensures
he sleeps enough.
Excellent!

Good on you Elliot (and Emma, Edvard, Ethan and Eliza).

How about you?
Are you energetic too?